Geolo...

at

Hartland Quay

HOW TO USE THIS BOOK. This guide is designed for two audiences.

VISITORS to Hartland Quay who are fascinated by the magnificent cliffs and spectacularly folded rocks are provided with a straightforward explanation of the local rocks and their history. The even-numbered pages, on the left-hand side, are in bold print and provide a simple interpretation designed specifically for the interested non-specialist. If you are a visitor it is suggested that, after reading the introduction, you start the short walk using the commentary in bold print and simply dip as you wish into the more detailed discussion, given in finer print on the right-hand pages.

EDUCATIONAL GROUPS and those with some knowledge of geology will find the commentary, in bold type on the left-hand pages, gives directions for finding some of the most interesting locations in the bay. The finer print, on the right-hand pages, provides a deeper commentary on aspects of the geology and in particular provides reference notes for examining the variety of structures exhibited in this dramatic section of the Crackington Formation. Detail in the text assumes some knowledge of the subject but there is a deliberate attempt to make explanations accessible to non-specialists.

THE INTRODUCTION to the walk is provided at both levels of commentary. This is best read before the walk. However, if you wish to start the walk immediately, then turn to page 10, but please first read the warnings on the front inside cover concerning SAFETY.

May 1989

INTRODUCTION

The geological time-scale and drifting continents

At Hartland Quay two major types of rock, sandstones and mudstones, have been folded to form some of the most spectacular coastal scenery and geology in North West Europe. Here we can investigate evidence of dramatic geological events that took place on the earth's surface over 300 million years ago. In order to appreciate the vastness of the geological time scale, note that the Earth formed 4,500 million years ago (A). The oldest surviving rocks in the world are about 4,000 million years old (B). Abundant remains of organisms (fossils) are first found in rocks laid down about 600 million years ago (C). During the walk we will be following the history of Devon over the past 400,000,000 years (D), a fraction of the world's history.

Time (Millions of years before the present)

4500 4000 3500 3000 2500 2000 1500 1000 500 0

A   B   C D

The continents of today are not fixed, but are embedded in areas of the Earth's crust which drift around on the surface of the globe as 'plates' floating on the semi-molten mantle beneath the crust. When the rocks of Hartland Quay were laid down, this location was somewhere near the equator.

Separation of plates creates oceans; collision of plates creates mountains. Figure 1 shows how the continental plates around Britain have drifted over the past 400 million years. Note that between 400 and 300 million years ago South West England was being squeezed between two gigantic colliding continental plates.

Figure 1. A highly stylised map of the drifting of the continents over the past 400 million years.

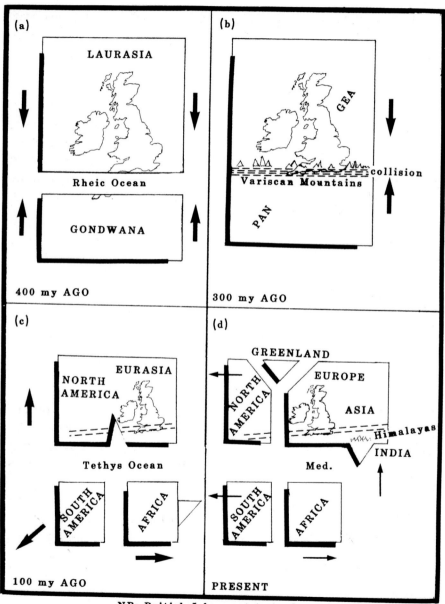

NB: British Isles not to scale

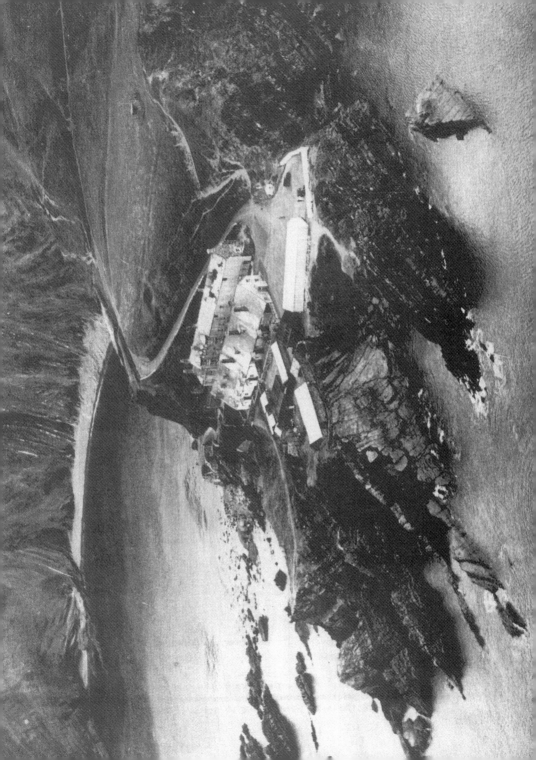

Stratigraphy and plate tectonics

The rocks exposed at Hartland Quay consist of a series of sediments, mainly fine-grained sandstones and mudstones, which were originally deposited as sands and muds about 320 million years ago during the Carboniferous Period (Figure 3). The sediments deposited in the area which now forms Hartland Quay are called the Crackington Formation.

Figure 3 The geological time scale showing the age of the Carboniferous rocks of North Devon and the local formation names.

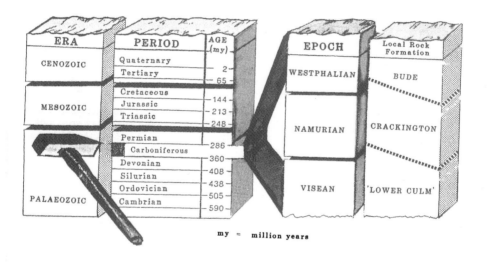

my = million years

About 350 million years ago in Carboniferous times, 'Devon' as we know it, lay on the southern margin of the major northern continent, Laurasia (figure 1). Laurasia was separated from the southern continental landmass of Gondwana by an ocean that geologists have called the Rheic Ocean.

Some 300 million years ago a collision of the two super-continents caused the closing of the Rheic Ocean and for a time the world's continents fused to become one super-continent, named Pangea (figure 1). This continental collision produced the compression of the intervening basins, together with the sediments within them. The result was the formation of the Variscan mountain chain which stretched across, and to the south of, the area we now call North Devon.

◄ Figure 2. Air photo of Hartland Quay 1932 (Aerofilms Ltd)

5

INTRODUCTION The rocks are laid down.

What was happening in the area before the continental collision of 300 million years ago disturbed the rocks of North Devon?

The sedimentary rocks at Hartland Quay were being laid down as soft sands and muds on the floor of an inland sea or lake. To the south was an open ocean, whilst to the north was an area in which reef limestones, sands, muds and later, thick seams of peat (now coals) were deposited. The present coalfields of South Wales are part of this sequence.

Figure 4. The North Devon Basin in Carboniferous times. This figure represents South West England at that time from a viewpoint above Dartmoor (South Devon) looking northwards. The sea has been removed from the diagram so as to show the sea bed and the positions of the present-day towns of South West England.

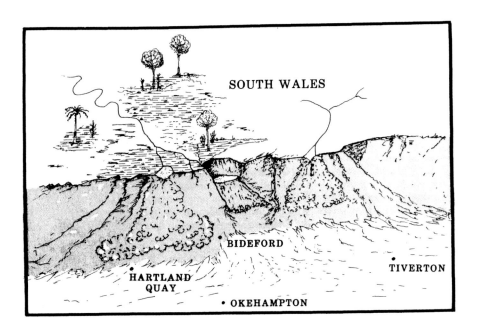

The Deposition of Sandstone and Shale Sequences

To understand the nature of the Carboniferous sediments which created the rocks of Hartland Quay, it is necessary to appreciate something of the depositional processes then operating, and the contemporary geography, referred to as the palaeo-geography. Figures 4 and 5 both illustrate the palaeo-geography of South West England during the Carboniferous.

At that time, before the continental collision which finally closed the Rheic Ocean, the Hartland area was located within a basin which probably contained fresh water and was, for the most part, separated from the sea. However, occasional marine incursions into the basin allowed marine organisms such as goniatites (photo page 20) to invade the area.

The thick layers of the Carboniferous sediments found in North Devon (2-3 km or 7,000-10,000 ft) suggest that the basin floor must have been subsiding during this period. Rivers flowed into the basin, bringing with them coarse sands together with finer silts and clays. These sediments were sorted by submarine currents and deposited in layers or beds on the essentially flat floor of the basin.

Figure 5. A schematic north-south section across the North Devon Basin during the Carboniferous period.

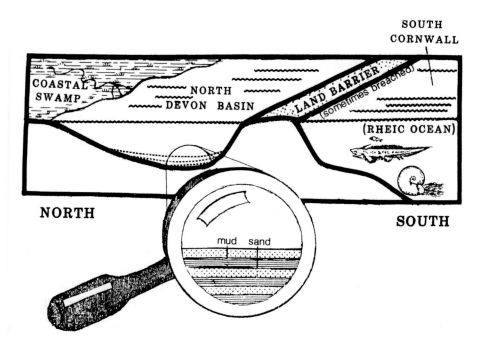

INTRODUCTION Compressing the Rocks

In North Devon the collision of the northern and southern continents (figure 1b) compressed the sediments, to produce folds, and cracked (fractured) them to produce faults (figure 6). These folded and faulted rocks were then squeezed up to form a mountain chain similar in scale to the present day Alps or Himalayas. The Himalayas, for example, have been formed over the last 10 million years as a result of a collision between the northward drifting Indian plate and the Asian plate. (figure 1d).

Figure 6. Simple folds and faults in layered sedimentary rocks

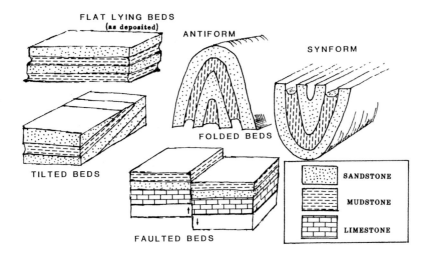

Folds are the result of compression (pushing together), but faults can result from either compression or tension (pulling apart). At Hartland Quay many minor fractures are clearly visible because the line of the fracture is 'picked out' with veins of quartz, a hard white mineral which has infilled many of the cracks caused by tension.

Tectonics; the study of the deformation of rocks

The mechanism by which the Continental and Oceanic Crust moves over the asthenosphere is not fully understood. We know that new ocean floor, formed from a basaltic lava, is generated along the Mid Ocean Ridge systems, thus causing the continents on either side to move further apart (see arrows in figure 7). As new ocean floor is generated, old ocean floor must be consumed (or subducted) if the earth is to stay a constant diameter.

Ocean floor basalts, together with any overlying sediments, are consumed in Subduction Zones. It is now known that very deep oceanic trenches develop along these subduction zones.

Figure 7. A stylised section through the earth showing the movement of 'plates' of oceanic and continental crust.

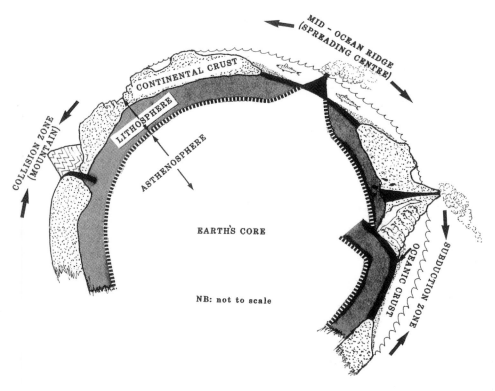

The North Devon Basin, in which the Carboniferous sands and muds were deposited, formed to the north of the main Rheic Ocean. The sediments were being laid down while continental collision and mountain-building occurred to the south. As the focus of compression moved north, the North Devon sediments were compressed and folded in the final stages of the Variscan mountain building event to produce the folded structures so dramatically exposed at Hartland Quay.

STARTING THE WALK. Open out the cover to reveal the map locating the stops on the walk. The extended outside cover gives a panorama of Warren Beach from the beginning of the walk.

1. THE SLIPWAY Panorama of Warren Beach

The spectacular cliffs of Warren Beach are the result of Atlantic storms. At high tides the waves erode the base of the cliffs eventually causing parts of the undercut cliff to collapse. This has exposed a clear section through typical rocks of the district. The rocks have a stripy appearance and are folded. Notice two types of fold. In the centre of the bay are a series of tight (zigzag or chevron-type) folds. At the sides of the bay are more gentle (open) folds.

Have the folds affected the way the cliffs have eroded? Consider this when you walk along the beach. The question can be picked up again at stop 7.

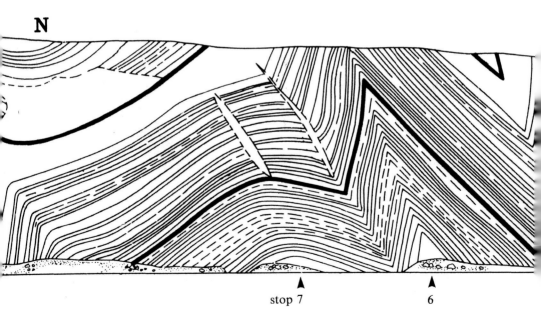

stop 7   6

Folding in the cliffs

The folding in the cliffs as viewed from the Slipway is impressive, particularly when it is remembered that these beds were originally laid down in near-horizontal layers. To get a clearer idea of the degree and complexity of the folding involved, select a prominent bed and follow it by eye across the cliff face as it is folded up and down. Do this and then check your ideas against figure 8.

The British Geological Survey (Edmunds and co-workers, 1979) in their description of this area, traced the detailed path of each bed of rock in the Warren Beach cliff (figure 8). The 'Hartland Quay Shale', shown as the lowest band emphasised in black in their sketch, is an easily identifiable horizon, and demonstrates the folding well. Shale is a fine-grained mudstone, which splits easily along closely-spaced bedding surfaces and can be seen from several of the stops on the walk (figure 8).

Now look at the folds more closely. Note that there are smaller, 'parasitic', folds on the limbs of the larger structures. There is a good example above the X marked on figure 8. The question of how folds develop and change perpendicular to the beds is one of the more complex concepts currently of interest to structural geologists.

Figure 8. An accurate sketch of the beds exposed in the Warren Beach cliff (reproduced with permission of the Director of the BGS. Crown/NERC copyright reserved)

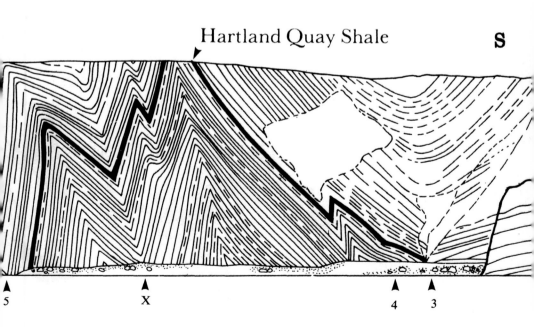

Hartland Quay Shale

2. THE TUNNEL SLAB

Now leave the slipway and walk along the beach a few metres to the tilted slab of rock illustrated in figure 9. As with the folded beds viewed from the slipway, these layers of tilted rocks were once flat-lying sediments on a sea or lake floor. Because the rocks are layered and were deposited as sands and muds they are termed 'sedimentary' rocks. At site 2 these beds are steeply tilted. An unusually thick bed of mudstone has eroded to leave the tunnel.

At site 2 we can examine the rocks close up and, using the table below, distinguish between the sandstones and mudstones which are responsible for the stripy appearance of the cliff.

Rock type	Colour	Hardness	Grain size	Comments
SANDSTONE	Light grey or rusty brown	Very hard, brittle	Coarse (rough to touch)	Massive featureless beds
MUDSTONES (shale) (shillet)	Dark grey-black	Softer, scrapes with knife	Fine (smooth to touch)	Thinner layered beds

Figure 9. Tunnel Slab viewed from the foot of the slipway

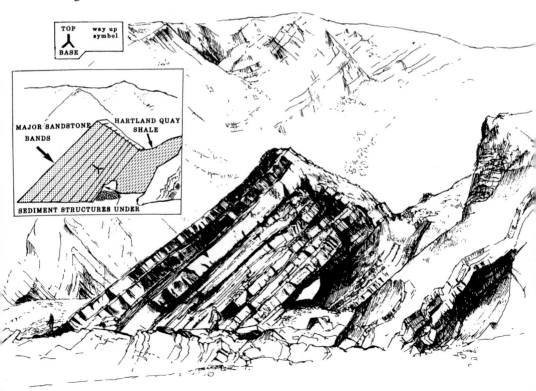

Aspects of sedimentology and structure

Examining the sediments at Tunnel Slab will reveal that they consist of alternations of softer, darker finer-grained mudstones and harder, coarser, lighter-coloured sandstones. The sandstones are sometimes a rusty-brown due to surface oxidation of iron-rich minerals.

What does the sequence of alternating finer and coarser sediments suggest about the velocity of the currents supplying the sediments?

What mechanism could have deposited these sediments in this way?

Figure 10. Idealised section through a turbidite sequence

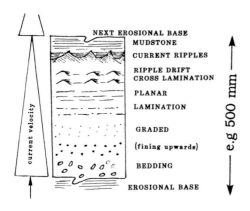

The size of sedimentary particles which can be transported by a current is dependent upon the velocity of that current. The higher the velocity the larger the particles that can be carried. Variations in grain size of a sedimentary rock sequence (e.g. sandstones and mudstones) therefore suggest variations in current velocity. From field observation and laboratory experiments, it is thought that such sedimentary sequences are the result of deposition from 'turbidity currents'.

Turbidity currents

Mud and sand on a submarine slope can be put into suspension by shock waves which may be generated by a major storm or earthquake. This slurry then moves downslope as a strong sea-floor current (figure 4, page 6). Initially this 'turbidity current' will move rapidly at speeds of up to 60-80 mph (100-140 km/h), but its velocity will decrease as the sea-floor gradient lessens. As the current velocity falls the sediment grains will be deposited. At any particular location along its route, first the coarsest grains, and then progressively finer particles will accumulate. Consequently, coarser, denser sediment, such as sand, will be overlain by finer, less dense material such as silt. As the turbidity current finally wanes it will deposit mud. The further the location is from the initial source of the current, the higher will be the proportion of fine-grained sediments.

The time between one turbidite depositional event and the next will be highly variable, but may be measured in tens, if not hundreds of thousands of years. Each such event however, will result in a sedimentary unit with coarser material at the base and finer at the top. Repeated turbidity current episodes can create a sequence of graded beds which will consolidate into alternating beds of sandstones and mudstones.

The North Devon Basin (figure 5, page 7) is believed to have been a basin which received sediments in this way with down slope and possibly axial (coast parallel) turbidites developed. Owing to variations in the depositional processes, only parts of the idealised sequence may be preserved. Examine the sediments closely including the junctions between the different rock layers or beds (the bedding surfaces). How closely do these compare with the sequence illustrated in figure 10?

Underwater flows of sand/mud slurries

The situation in which the sands and muds were first laid down is illustrated on page 6 (figure 4). It is thought that much of the sediment descended from the steep underwater slope in the north of the basin in the form of 'slurry-mixtures' of sand and mud, probably triggered by violent storms or earthquakes.

If the tide is out you can demonstrate the principle of such 'turbidite flow' in any beach pool which has a sandy edge. Stamp your foot, or stir up the sand with your hand and watch the slurry flow down the slope to settle on the flat bottom of the pool.

Figure 11. A do-it-yourself turbidite experiment in a sandy pool at Hartland Quay

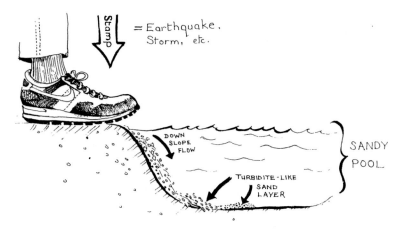

On a very different scale you can imagine how, over a long period, millions of tonnes of sediments could have been swept down into the basin thought to have occupied North Devon in Carboniferous times. As the turbidity currents slowed down on the gentler off-shore slopes, the heavier sands settled-out before the muds and so the mixture in any particular turbidite sequence was sorted into beds of sand and muds. The sandstones and mudstones in these cliffs are believed to have formed in this way.

Details of structures which commonly occur in turbidite sequences

When beds have been strongly folded it may not be obvious in which order they were originally deposited. Sediments deposited by turbidity currents frequently display 'way-up' criteria, which allow the determination of the 'younging' direction and, in some cases, provide information about the direction of sediment transport.

Examine the upper and lower surfaces of the sandstone beds seen at stop 2 and try to identify some of the structures illustrated below. Do not venture into the tunnel without a helmet. Some of these structures can be identified at other stops along the walk.

Figure 12 Common 'sole structures' in turbidites

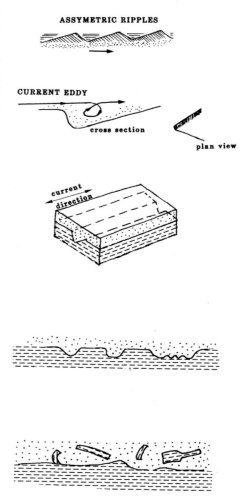

1. Ripple marks are formed by currents. Asymmetry or cross bedding seen in cross-section may indicate direction of flow.

ASSYMETRIC RIPPLES

2. Flute casts are narrow 'arrow-shaped' structures formed when the current transporting the sand develops eddies which scour hollows in the underlying semi-consolidated mud. The closed end of the cast always points up-current. Eddies may be associated with objects (pebbles, etc.) on the sea floor.

CURRENT EDDY

cross section

plan view

3. Groove casts are linear ridges formed as a result of hard objects (e.g. mud flakes or plant debris) carried along in the sand-depositing current cutting grooves or 'tool marks' in the top of the underlying mud. These grooves are now preserved as casts on the base of the overlying, harder, sandstone units. The groove runs parallel to the direction of current flow (photo, page 27).

current direction

4. Load casts are rather bulbous, lobate structures. They are formed by the denser sand 'loading down' into the less dense mud beneath. Load casts exhibit a wide variety of hummocky forms and may, as at stop 2, look like elephant or rhino hide (photo, page 27).

5. Mudflake conglomerates are small fragments of mudstone preserved near the base of the sandstone where currents have ripped the semi-consolidated muds on the sea floor and carried the mudflakes down-current to be deposited with the turbidite sand.

3. THE GULLY

Now continue north across the cobbles and boulders for about 100 metres. If the tide is not too high, stop at the large gully, which runs out from the cliff, crossing the rocks towards the sea. Figure 13 shows the view from the gully looking towards the cliffs. Note the steep sides to the gully and its width, about 5 metres (18 feet) at this point. Look carefully at one side of the gully. Do the beds of rock on this side of the gully seem match across to those on the opposite side of the gully? How would you describe the match?

Figure 13. Looking north-east
across the gully from stop 3

On the Hartland Quay side of the gully, the rock beds dip steeply to the north, the same structure as the Tunnel Slab (stop 2). On the north (Warren Beach) side of the gully, the beds are contorted into a set of chevron folds, the forms of which can be traced back across the rocks and into the cliff face (figure 13). The very different structures on opposite sides of the gully suggest that we are standing on a major fracture zone or fault. It seems likely that this straight gully has been eroded by the sea, exploiting the line of weakness created by the fault.

Faults

Faults result from the rapid release of built-up pressure within the earth's crust producing fractures, or fracture zones, which allow the movement of the rock sequence on one side of the fracture relative to the other.

Figure 14 Four styles of faulting

A normal fault is one in which the 'hanging wall' appears to have moved down relative to the 'foot wall'. A reverse fault is one in which the 'hanging wall' appears to have moved up in relation to the 'foot wall'. In both cases the angle of the fault plane is usually between 45 and 90 degrees.

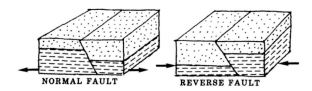

NORMAL FAULT   REVERSE FAULT

Rocks may also be displaced laterally by 'wrench faults' under either extension or compression. Examples of this type of fault are not seen at Hartland Quay. Thrust faults may result from compression (e.g. continental collision), or from rock masses sliding under the influence of gravity as mountain chains are uplifted.

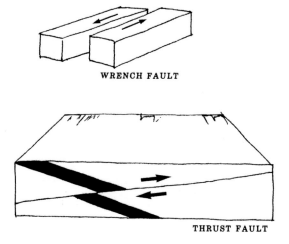

WRENCH FAULT

THRUST FAULT

Folding and faulting in North Devon took place mainly during the Variscan Orogenic event (figure 1b, page 3) and occurred deep within the mountain chain relatively soon after the deposition and deep burial of the sediments.

4. UNSTABLE CLIFFS

Now follow the fault along the gully towards the cliff for a short way until the view is similar to that in figure 15. Look at the cliff here. Has the fault had any noticable affect on the shape of the cliff at this point? For example, compare the cliff shape here with the cliffs further along the bay to the left (north).

Figure 15. The cliffs as seen from near stop 4

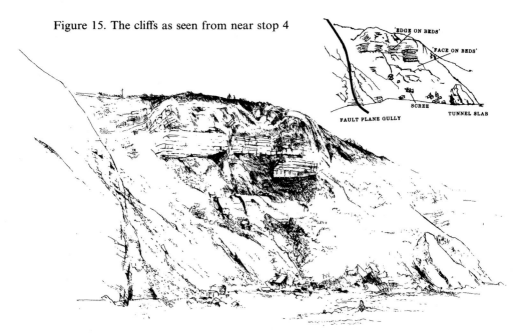

This area of unstable and slumped cliff is typical of what happens when a fault line cuts a cliff. Just as the sea has exploited the fault line on the shore to erode a gully, so weathering and erosion on the land have also taken advantage of the weak fault zone, breaking up the cliff to form a shallow notch or valley. The loose rock debris falls to produce a scree.

Another factor which makes the cliffs particularly unstable here is that in places the rock beds slope steeply seawards (some slope at about 60 degrees). This encourages any rock loosened by weathering, to slide down towards the beach.

Other factors controlling cliff stability

Strike

In this district of steeply-dipping beds, cliff profiles differ dramatically depending upon whether the beds strike parallel or at right angles (perpendicular) to the coast (figure 16). On the Hartland Quay coast the beds run straight out to sea and this in general encourages clean, upright cliffs. A short distance away on the Clovelly coast, the strike of the rock is often parallel to the shore and, particularly where the beds dip seawards, the cliffs tend to slump untidily towards the sea.

Exposure

A further consideration is the degree of exposure of the cliffs to storm waves. The north-east facing coast of the district, near Clovelly, is relatively sheltered from Atlantic storms, and cliff falls and screes are slow to be removed by waves of comparatively low energy. The screes protect the cliff-foot from further wave attack.

The west-facing coast of the Hartland district, is pounded by Atlantic waves of high energy. Such waves rapidly remove screes and fallen rock debris, exposing the cliff-foot to fresh undercutting and so encouraging the persistence of steep cliffs. However, there are considerable local variations. The cliff above stop 4 is in the most sheltered part of Warren Bay and the structure here has led to a cliff profile which is not typical of this stretch of coast.

Figure 16 The effect of strike and exposure on cliffs in the Hartland area.

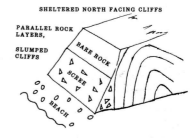

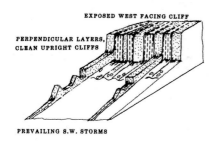

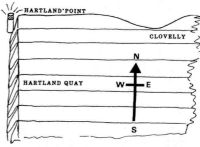

Composition

What the rock is made of, its composition, is also critical in determining the cliff profile. Some rocks are more resistant to weathering and erosion than others. Scrutiny of the foreshore or of the rocks of Tunnel Slab should emphasise the differential resistance of sandstone and mudstone. On the beach the sandstone beds form prominent ridges whilst the mudstones have eroded into elongated rock pools and 'furrows'.

FOSSILS

You may have been disappointed at the apparent lack of fossils in these rocks. Geologists too would like to find more fossils. The preserved forms of long-dead animals and plants help to date the rocks since, owing to continuous evolution, particular fossil forms are associated with particular periods of the earth's history.

The few fossils that are found do not seem to have lived permanently in the deep basin in which the rocks of Hartland Quay were laid down. Goniatites, ancient relatives of today's Nautilus, seem to have come in from the open sea. Fossil land plants such as Equisetum, very similar to the present 'horse tail' must have been washed into the basin originally from nearby land.

Figure 17. (a) A pebble on the beach at Hartland Quay providing a natural section through a goniatite. (b) A slab from a fossil plant bed in Warren Beach Bay. (c) Phosphatic fish debris and coprolites (faecal pellets).

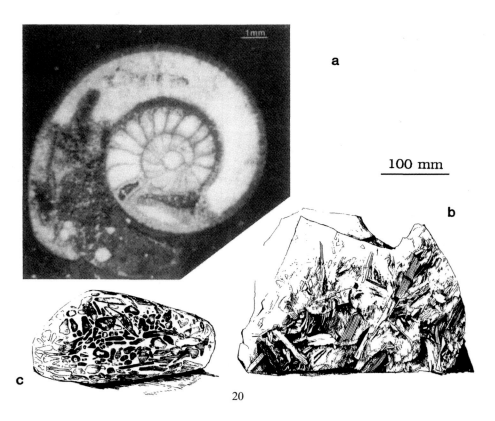

Palaeo-ecology and fossil preservation

Why are there few fossils in the sediments at Hartland Quay? An absence of fossils can mean one of a number of things:

* Perhaps no animals or plants were present in the waters overlying the site of the sediment deposition.
* Perhaps no animals lived on or in the sediment itself owing to 'poisonous' conditions or an unstable sediment surface.
* Perhaps no organisms were brought in by currents from adjacent shelf areas or land.
* Perhaps organisms were present but not preserved, possibly being destroyed by scavengers, current activity or during burial and compaction.
* Perhaps you could suggest other options?

Which of these conditions seems to best fit the Carboniferous Basin of North Devon? Opinions differ as to which explanation is most probable, but the almost total absence of trace fossils (bioturbation) in the sediments suggests a lack of bottom-living animals, possibly because the deep water of the basin was stagnant and lacking in dissolved oxygen.

The fossils we do find seem to have been carried in from outside the basin, as in the case of the goniatites which lived in the open sea, and the plant remains which were swept in from adjacent land masses. There is no evidence for life in the deep waters of the North Devon Basin. Fossil trails (but not 'body' fossils) of an early form of King Crab have been reported from rocks of approximately this age near Bude, but the trails appear to suggest animals trying to escape from the deep basin environment having been swept down-slope by turbidites originating on the shallow basin margins.

The almost complete absence of stratigraphically useful fossils makes dating these sediments problematical. The age shown in figure 3, page 5, is only approximate, being constrained by the very limited number of useful goniatite-bearing horizons in these sediments.

Figure 18 A possible explanation of the 'goniatite bands' in the Carboniferous rocks of North Devon

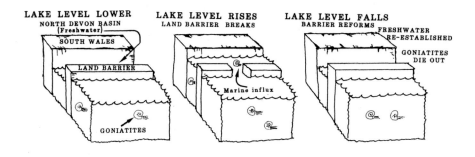

21

5. A DOWNFOLD

REMINDER The cliffs north of here are dangerous. Do not approach them without a helmet and then only with extreme caution.

Now walk northwards along the beach until you can view the downfold (a synform) illustrated in figure 19. The layers of sediments, originally near-horizontal, have been tightly folded. Folds like this are good evidence for continental collision.

Look at the way that the thicker sandstone is bent around the sharpest point of the fold. How could this happen in such hard, brittle rock?

Figure 19. The Warren Beach synform

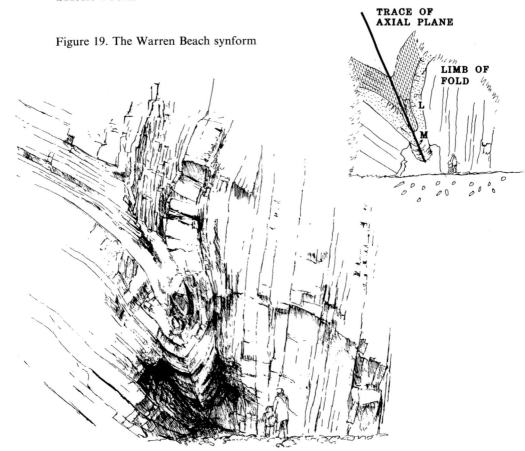

Folding without cracking

Examination of the axis of the tight synform at stop 5 shows that the now brittle sandstone beds have been bent through as much as 300 degrees without cracking. How is this possible?

The most likely explanation is that under the pressure of folding, solution of some sand (quartz) grains took place in areas of high pressure (the limb of the fold), and that this material migrated and was redeposited into areas of lower pressure (axis of the fold). To verify this two samples of sandstone were taken from the synform at stop 5. One was taken from the axis (point M on figure 19) and the other from the limb of the fold (point L in figure 19). Thin sections of the samples were cut and photographed down a microscope.

Both photographs (figure 20) show details of the grains. The large white areas in photo M (axis of fold) are patches where quartz has been redeposited from solution. Photo L (limb of fold) does not show these patches, but instead shows apparently flattened, elongated grains which have been formed by some material being dissolved away. Thus, it seems likely that material has been moved in solution away from the fold limbs and into the fold axis.

Figure 20. Photomicrographs of sandstone collected at stop 5

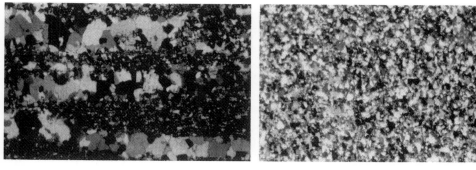

M (axis)   L (limb)

Rocks react differently to stress depending upon how brittle or ductile they are. At Hartland Quay there is a sequence of alternating relatively brittle (or competent) sandstones interbedded with more ductile (plastically deforming) mudstones and shales. When examining the folds, notice that the competent sandstone beds maintain a more or less constant thickness around the hinge of the fold. However, as a result of the development of tension cracks, spaced or fracture cleavages often occur roughly at right angles to the bedding surfaces. The spaced cleavage is frequently infilled with quartz.

The more incompetent mudstones or shales flow into the hinge of the fold, producing a thinning of the limbs. The mudstones develop a much finer, slatey cleavage parallel to the axial surface of the fold. This results from the realignment of the tiny flakes of the clay minerals in the mudstones.

SANDSTONE
(spaced cleavage
often quartz filled)

MUDSTONE
(slatey cleavage)

23

REVIEW OF THE GEOLOGICAL HISTORY

The evidence seen so far on the walk supports detailed geological research suggesting that the area has experienced four main stages in its evolution, as illustrated below. As is usual in geological drawings, the first (oldest) stage is illustrated at the bottom and the last (youngest) at the top.

Figure 21. Stages in the evolution of Hartland Quay

Stage 4. Uplift to expose the rocks as seen at the present day land surface.

Stage 3. Folding and Faulting of compacted sandstones and mudstones.

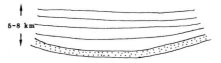

Stage 2. Burial and compaction of sand and mud to 5-8 km in the earth's crust.

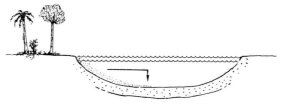

Stage 1. Deposition of sands and mud on the floor of the North Devon Basin.

The geometry of folds

Useful terms used in the description
of folds include:

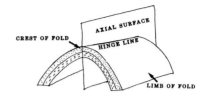

Depending upon the angle of the limbs relative to the axial surface, folds may be described as follows:

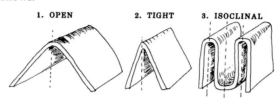

Folds may also be described using the angle of the axial surface relative to the horizontal:

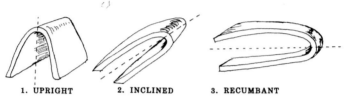

Characterising folds

Folds may be antiformal or synformal. They may be anticlinal or synclinal. The first two terms refer simply to the shape of the folds, antiforms being upfolds and synforms being downfolds. The second two terms refer to the sequence in age of the rocks within the folds. Anticlines have the oldest rocks in the core, synclines have the youngest rocks in the core. In most areas of relatively straightforward folding, the antiforms will also be anticlines and the synforms will be synclines. This is illustrated below, where A is the oldest rock bed and C is the youngest rock bed.

1 An antiformal (upfolded) anticline (oldest rock in core).

2 A synformal (downfolded) syncline (youngest rock in core).

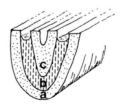

Now hold the book upside down and then attempt to describe the folds.

1 now becomes a synformal anticline.

2 becomes an antiformal syncline.

6. AN UPFOLD

Continue to the northern end of the beach. Here the rocks are folded up into a pointed arch (figure 22). This upfolded structure is called an antiform as the rocks point upwards. Select an easily recognisable bed and, by eye, follow the bed up one side of the fold, over the crest and down the other side.

At the crest of the fold you may have had some difficulties. Why was this? A fault has developed along the tight crest of this antiform. The beds to the right (south) appear to have been pushed upwards along this fault plane.

Why has a cave formed here? The crest of the fold and the fault plane are zones of weakness encouraging wave erosion in this less sheltered corner of the bay. The cathedral-like roof of the cave provides natural support.

Figure 22. The antiform and cave at stop 6

Gathering more information on sandstone deposition

On the steeply dipping left limb of the fold, a sandstone bed forms a rib running out onto the foreshore (on the left of figure 22). An examination of the structures on this bedding surface should reveal whether you are looking at the base or top of this sandstone bed.

The diagnostic structures are all listed in the table on page 15, and at least three of these should be recognisable at this stop; load casts, groove casts and flute casts.

Because all these structures are preserved on the base of sandstone units, they are collectively referred to as 'sole structures' and constitute important 'way-up criteria'.

Figure 23 Groove casts and load casts at stop 6

7. AN OPEN FOLD

If the tide is rising, turn back at stop 6 and return to the slipway (stop 8). Otherwise, if you are able-bodied, continue north by walking down the beach some 30 metres and then clambering through a breach in the major sandstone rib which blocks your way. Immediately beyond is an open 'barrel-vaulted' cave (figure 24). This gentle open fold is unusual for North Devon.

In the roof and floor of the cave are lines of a white mineral. These are fractures in the rock which have been infilled with quartz deposited from percolating watery solutions. In places the quartz veins pick out 'tension gashes', lines where the rocks have been torn apart, showing an 'en echelon' pattern.

Figure 24. The cave at stop 7.

The anatomy of a fold

Turn to the outside cover of the booklet and locate the open fold at stop 7 on the panoramic sketch of Warren Beach cliff. The southern end of the bay also has an open fold. Between these, the central area of cliff has tight zig-zag (chevron) folds. All of these structures seem to have been formed during the same folding event, and show how difficult it is to predict the way that rocks will deform.

With your back to the cave, trace the crest of the antiform across the rocky shore towards the sea. What is happening to the dip of the beds as the crest of the antiform is followed seawards?

Figure 25. Looking towards the sea from stop 6

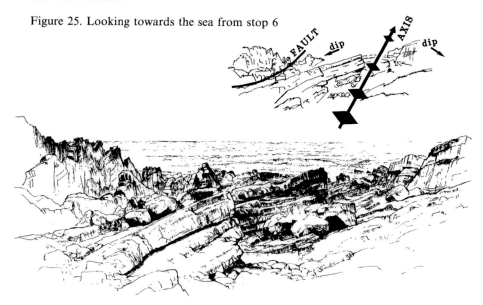

The antiform is 'plunging' towards the west (seawards). The plunge is measured as the angle between the hinge line and the horizontal. Because marine erosion has sliced near-horizontally across this plunging antiform it is well-displayed in plan.

The interpretation of folding is often complicated by faulting. A good example of the complex three-dimensional interaction of a low-angle fault and a fold can be found at the back of the cave.

29

8. AN OVERTURNED FOLD

As you walk take time to examine the pebbles and boulders beneath your feet. They are the product of 'abrasion', the incessant wearing away of stone against stone. Most of the pebbles, polished by attrition, originated from the hard, grey local sandstone. There are many interesting shapes and textures. The grey pebbles may be enhanced by white quartz-filled fractures, sometimes revealing themselves as white circles standing slightly proud of the pebble surface. Occasionally the polished grey surface emphasises a cluster of dark grey mud flakes or more rarely an identifiable fossil.

Pause at the foot of the slipway and look left (east) at the rock face below the small fisherman's shelter. Here the beds have been so strongly folded that the upper (left-hand) limb has been bent right over to produce an overturned fold, figure 26.

Figure 26. The overturned fold at the foot of the slipway, site 8

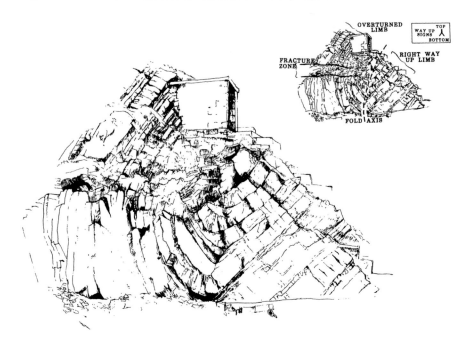

Complex folding

The fold at stop 8 has been partially turned over and may be called a overturned or recumbent fold. However, it is still synformal, i.e. the two limbs tilt towards each other downwards. It is also synclinal because the youngest rocks are in the core (see page 25). If the overturning of this fold had been complete, then it would have become an 'antiform', and yet would still be a syncline because the youngest rocks would still be in the core. To be exact, such a fold would be called an antiformal syncline.

In areas where folding is complex one cannot take it for granted that the fold is 'the right way up'. How might you confirm that the fold at stop 8 is a synformal syncline? Since 'sole structures' (page 15) are always preserved on the 'bases' of the sandstone beds, they can be used as 'way-up' criteria to determine whether the sediments are in the same order as when laid down, or whether they have been overturned as a result of tilting or folding. This is very useful information when interpreting the structural development of highly deformed strata.

Slickensides

A noticeable feature of the folding at Hartland Quay is the development of 'scratches' on the bedding planes of the folded rocks. Bend this booklet slowly into a U-shaped fold and notice how the pages move against one another as they adjust to the new structure. The marks on the bedding surfaces, called 'slickensides' or 'stretching lineation', were formed by similar adjustments as the rock layers slid over one another when forming folds or faults. The mudstones are the more plastic and 'lubricative' of the rock types found here, and hence slickensides generally occur on sandstone surfaces adjacent to the mudstone. There may also be some quartz along the junction which was remobilised as a result of solution during deformation.

If you rub your finger along the 'scratch', one direction should feel rough and the other smooth. The 'smooth' direction is the direction of movement of the overlying bed. If found on a fault plane surface, slickensides can similarly indicate the direction of movement of the fault.

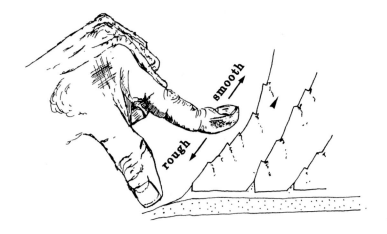

9. SLIPWAY LOOKING WEST

Now climb about a third of the way up the slipway until, if the tide is out, the view west is similar to that in figure 27. The walk is now almost completed, so do you feel confident enough to recognise the folds and faults in this rocky foreshore? AFTER you have studied the view, check your conclusions against the inset diagram at the bottom of the page!

Figure 27. The view west from the slipway at low tide

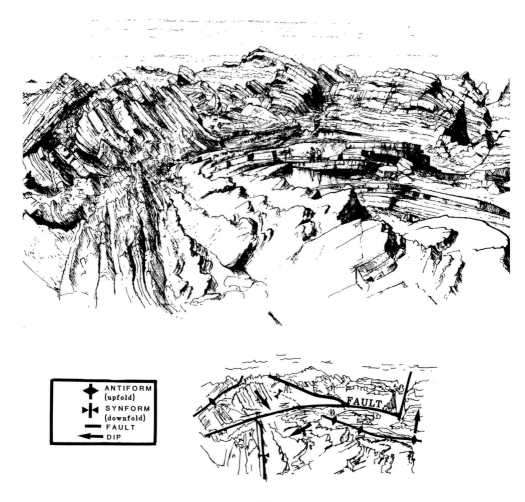

ANTIFORM (upfold)
SYNFORM (downfold)
FAULT
DIP

A plunging antiform - try your hand at structural geology

For those equipped with a compass-clinometer, and providing the tide is out, the shore west of the slipway (figure 27) is a useful area to try out one or two simple data gathering exercises that are important prerequisites for geological interpretation. Before you start the exercise ensure that you clearly understand the terms 'dip' and 'strike' (see below).

1. Stand on any obviously tilted bedding surface and measure both strike and dip. Do strike first. Remember that you are measuring the compass direction of a horizontal line on the bed, so you must start by determining the exact position of the horizontal line. With a little ingenuity you can use the clinometer to determine this - it is, of course, a line with an inclination of 0 degrees. Having marked (using, for example, a knife to scratch) the horizontal line, measure its compass direction (between 0 and 180 degrees).

2. Record this measurement. Now, using a clinometer, measure the dip amount, at 90 degrees to the strike. Record this amount also. You now have two numbers, a strike direction and a dip amount. You can combine these in one mapping symbol as follows:

dip amount 14

strike direction

(dip amount with the 'tick' indicating the direction, 90 degrees to the strike)

3. Once you are confident of this, move to the antiform illustrated in figure 27 and make a series of measurements of dip and strike starting on one side of the antiform, and moving around to the other side. Work in a semicircle from the north side, first moving seawards and up the bedding surface to the crest and then downwards and away from the sea. If you make a sketch map of the dips and strikes, they should give this pattern:

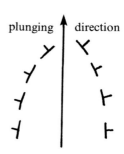

plunging ↑ direction

4. The pattern is distinctive. It is a plunging antiform. What would be the pattern for a synform plunging towards the sea?

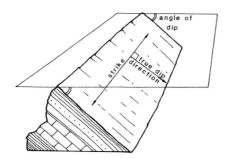

angle of dip

strike

true dip direction

Dip and Strike

The direction of **STRIKE** of an inclined surface is the compass direction of a horizontal line on the surface, measured between 0 and 180 degrees.

The amount of true **DIP** is the angle of downward inclination of an inclined surface measured at right angles to the strike.

10. LOWER CAR PARK

Now continue up the slipway and walk back past the hotel to the lower car park. The wall on the far side overlooks Well Beach. Like many beaches in North Devon the rocky foreshore exposed at low tide is remarkably flat. Both the steep cliff and the shore platform are the result of erosion by Atlantic storm-waves often armed with the hard grey pebbles derived from the local sandstone.

Figure 28 The evolution of the shore at Well Beach

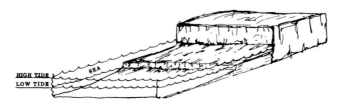

Stage 3. Over several thousand years of continuous attack the cliff line retreats and a wide wave-cut platform is developed.

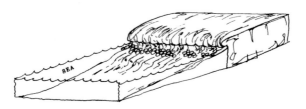

Stage 2. In time the shore is undercut creating cliffs and a narrow shelf where the cliff used to be.

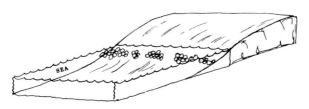

Stage 1. We must imagine the shore originally having no cliffs or wave-cut platform.

Creating geological maps and cross sections

Well Beach and the cliff behind provide a useful review of many of the features already examined during the walk. To summarise these, try drawing a geological cross-section combined with a geological map plotting the structures that are visible both in the cliff and on the beach. The cliff provides the cross-section whilst the beach shows the structures in plan. The two can be combined in one diagram as set out below.

Using conventional geological map symbols keeps the map neat and precise and immediately understood by other geologists. Some of the more common map symbols, in particular of those structures that can be seen at Well Beach, are illustrated below.

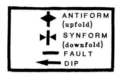

A framework for a field sketch map showing the geological structures at Well Beach.

cliff

foreshore

The folded rocks of Well Beach are a dramatic reminder of the enormous power of the continental collision which created these structures. Other processes continue to modify the landscape. The erosional processes which carved Well Beach and created the cliff face behind have not stopped.

Figure 29. Well Beach, October 1987

During the preparation of this booklet a massive cliff failure at Well Beach caused thousands of tonnes of rock debris to cascade down towards the beach. Figure 30 shows the landslide shortly after it happened. What changes have occurred since January 1988?

We would expect the sea to begin by removing all the finer material from the toe of the slip. Such undercutting might cause further collapse of cliff debris. The smaller angular sandstone blocks which have tumbled onto the beach can be moved by waves but are trapped in this bay. They will gradually be rounded into the hard grey sandstone pebbles so typical of the storm beach. In time only a 'lag deposit' of the largest blocks will remain, slowly being rounded and reduced in size by abrasion. Eventually the solid rock of the cliff-foot will once again be fully exposed to marine attack. Undercutting and the normal weathering and erosional processes of the land will inevitably encourage fresh rock-falls. What stage in the 'cycle' has been reached at the time of your visit?

Figure 30 Well Beach, January 1988

HARTLAND QUAY.

This is the end of the geological walk. Figure 31 shows the spectacular cliffs that you can see to the north of the Quay as you leave. All these cliffs are the result of coastal erosion. Consider how much rock material has been removed to create this cliff line. Where has all this rock gone? Much of it has been reduced to mud and sand and lies on the sea-bed preparing the next generation of rocks.

WHY STUDY FOLDS AND FAULTS?

Earth scientists are driven by intellectual curiosity to find out more about the history of rocks, but there are also clear economic reasons for their interest. Oil and gas are often trapped in structures created by folds and faults. Minerals which yield many important industrial metals are frequently found associated with faults. In addition the exploitation of roadstones, ball clay and coal all require a knowledge of the distribution of different sediment types and the effect of faults and folds.

FURTHER READING

Geology and landscape of the district:

The Geology of Devon. Edited by E.M. Durrence and D.J.C. Laming, University of Exeter, 1982.
The Geology of Bideford and Lundy Island. E.A. Edmonds, B.J. Williams and R.T. Taylor. Memoir of the Geological Survey of Great Britain, HMSO, 1979.
Classic Landforms of the North Devon Coast. Peter Keene, Geographical Association, Sheffield, 1986.

Texts on geological structure and sedimentology:

Minerals, Rocks and Fossils. W.R.Hamilton, A.R.Woodley & A.C.Bishop, Country Life Books, Hamlyn, 1974.
Foundations of Structural Geology. R.G.Park, Blackie, 1983.
Sedimentary Environments and Facies. Edited by H.J.Reading, Blackwell, 1978.
The Techniques of Modern Structural Geology, Volume 2 Folds and Fracturing. J.G. Ramsay & M.I. Huber, Academic Press London, 1987.
Britain Before Man. F.W. Dunning et al, Inst.Geol.Sci., HMSO, 1978,

Thematic Trails in Hartland District

Faced with the spectacular coastline of North West Devon many inquisitive visitors seek serious explanation for the dramatic landscapes of the area, and yet, being neither geologists nor geographers, are hesitant to read the specialist literature on the subject.

In three booklets, Thematic Trails introduces three different approaches to understanding the coastal scenery of the district. The explanation is serious, but it is the intention that each booklet may be read and understood by the interested non-specialist as well as those who may already have some knowledge of the themes explored.

In the first booklet, 'Geology at Hartland Quay', it is the rocks themselves which are explored. The second booklet, 'The Cliffs of Hartland Quay', investigates the shape or form of the coastal landscape. In the third booklet, 'Strawberry Water to Marsland Mouth', the emphasis is on the valleys, streams and beaches and what they can tell us about the recent past. These three approaches are combined in a broader view of the scenery of the district in the book 'Classic Landforms of the North Devon Coast'.

ACKNOWLEDGEMENTS

We should like to thank Margaret Peters for devotion beyond the call of duty in producing the pen-and-ink sketches in all weathers to meet our often impossible specifications of what ought to be there. We should also like to thank Alan Lewis for using his graphic ingenuity to produce the diagrams and insets.

Our thanks also go to Chris Topley for his many useful comments on the draft, for facilitating the production of the photomicrographs in the laboratories of Oxford Polytechnic Department of Geology and for his interpretation of the results.

Permission to reproduce Figure 8 (Warren Beach Cliff Section) from Edmonds et al., 1979, and the aerial photograph of Hartland Quay (Figure 2) is acknowledged from the Director of the British Geological Survey and Aerofilms Ltd. respectively.

Finally we should like to acknowledge the tremendous and sustained effort that Peter Keene (the editor of the series) has put into ensuring that this booklet has seen the light of day.

THEMATIC TRAILS and ASSOCIATED MATERIAL

Thematic Trails is an independent charitable trust, founded to make detailed, environmental interpretation in the field more accessible to interested visitors and non-specialists. Serious interpretation is often only possible with professional knowledge or with the use of academic literature which is often not readily available to the general public or to many teachers. The trust's main concern is to encourage an increased awareness of, and empathy for, the environment.

Central to this aim is the production of a series of thematic trails Each walk is a combined walk and reference booklet, the information being projected in such a way that it is stimulating, teaches something about the environment being explored, and is written to be understood by the curious, interested non-specialist. To further these aims , authors, authors and editor provide their services without charge. All money from the sale of trails and supporting material is recycled to meet the cost of publishing subsequent trails and associated literature.

North Devon Thematic Trail No 6   ISBN 0 948444 12 6